# The Night the Lights Went Out

by Robin Bloksberg
illustrated by René King Moreno

**D.C. Heath and Company**
Lexington, Massachusetts   Toronto, Ontario

It was a rainy night.
Jake was watching TV.

All of a sudden, the lights went out.
The TV went off, too!

"The lights are out!" said Jake.
"How will we see?"

His mother got flashlights.
She gave one to Jake.
"Oh, boy!" he said.

"The TV is off," said Jake.
"What can we do?"

"Let's read a book," said his mother.
"This is fun!" said Jake.

"The stove is off," said Jake.
"How can we cook?"

"Let's cook on the fireplace," said his mother.
"Awesome!" said Jake.

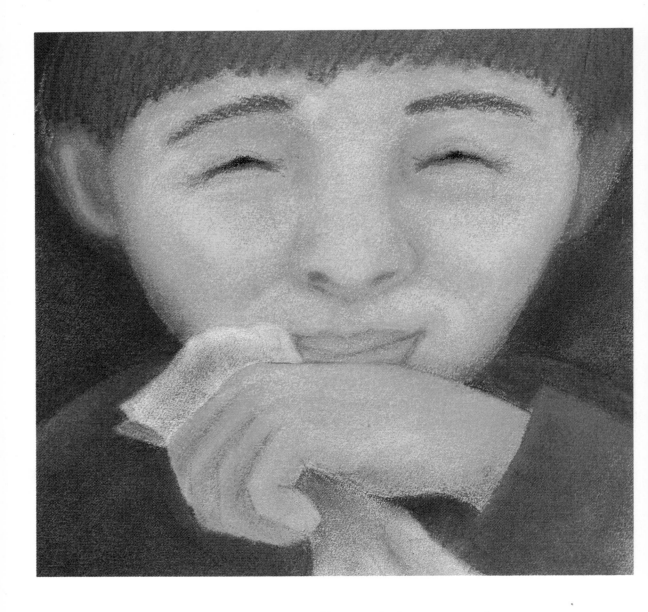

"Your face is a mess," said his mother.
"I can't wash it in the dark," said Jake.

"Oh, yes you can!" said his mother.

Then the lights came on.
The TV came on, too.

Do you know what Jake did?

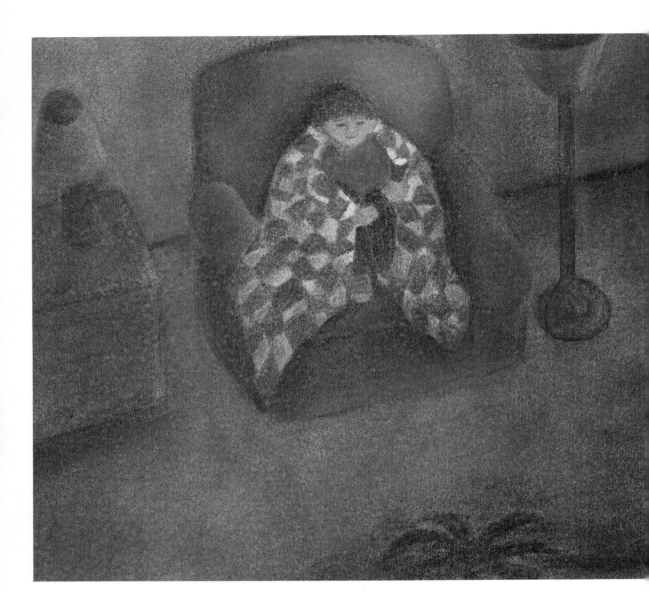

First he turned off the TV.

Next he turned off the lights.
Then he turned on the flashlight.

"It is more fun in the dark!" he said.